Heather Bennett-Smallwood

Illustrated by Andrew Laitinen

BETTER
Than a Bully

The POWER TO BE ME Series

LUCIDBOOKS

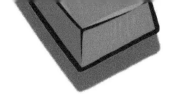

-DEDICATION-

To all who show kindness and respect to others
To teachers, for all that you do

-SPECIAL THANKS-

To my Lord and Savior
To my kind and courageous daughter, Jaelyn
To my sweet mom, Annie
To my friends and family, for your continued support

When I'm on the playground and things don't go my way,
I don't make the other kids be in the game I want to play.

I take my turn and listen to what my friends say.
We all have feelings that sometimes get in the way.

I'm not a bully. I don't offend.
I get along with others. I'm a true friend.

I spread positive vibes and give good advice.
I let people know when they are not being nice.

I'd rather be by myself and read a good book
than be with others who make fun of people's looks.

I'm not a bully. I don't offend.
I get along with others. I'm a true friend.

Calling people names because of the color of their skin
is hurtful to kids who could be really good friends.

Teasing people about the clothes they wear
is definitely not nice. It's really unfair.

I'm not a bully. I don't offend.
I get along with others. I'm a true friend.

Trying to joke with people by putting them down
is rude and mean, and it always makes me frown.

I include others when I am able
by making room at the lunchroom table.

I'm not a bully. I don't offend.
I get along with others. I'm a true friend.

I keep my hands and feet to myself.
I feel proud by not hurting someone else.

Using kind words and actions is very appealing.
I don't ever want to hurt another person's feelings.

Being a good friend makes me happy inside.
I like giving fist bumps and cool high fives!

I'm not a bully. I don't offend.
I get along with others. I'm a true friend.

Standing up for what I believe or sticking up for a friend
is caring and catchy. It can even start a trend!

Others will follow and do the same thing.
Can you imagine the joy it will bring?

Getting upset can happen with a friend.
Then I know to take a breath and count to ten.

This makes me feel better and proud in every way.
I can start all over because tomorrow is a new day!

Discussion after reading *Better Than a Bully*:

Ask children to recall examples from the book of how friends showed kindness.

Ask children what they learned from the book that will help them be a good friend, solve conflicts peacefully, and avoid bullying situations.

Art/Language Arts Extension Activities:

Have children role-play or use puppets to act out ways that they can show kindness in the lunchroom, on the playground, or in the classroom.

Have children create a mural or a comic strip with speech balloons from one or more of the stanzas in the book or on their own to demonstrate being a good friend.

Have children create a short video demonstrating how to show kindness or stick up for a friend.

Have children journal about a time when they witnessed someone not showing kindness or being a good friend, and how they resolved or could have resolved the situation.

Create a 3-column T-Chart with LOOKS Like, SOUNDS Like, and FEELS Like as column headings. Have children brainstorm words/phrases for showing kindness in each column.

Use the T-Shirt cut-out to have children create an illustration of their favorite part of the book, or have them create their own stanza for showing kindness.

About the Author:

A 17-year veteran educator with a bachelor's degree in psychology and a master's degree in education, Heather Bennett-Smallwood has taught in various schools across the US.

Bennett-Smallwood strongly believes in the importance of instilling self-awareness, confidence, and self-esteem in young boys and girls to help them grow into confident, emotionally healthy, and thriving adults. She believes everyone has the ability to overcome obstacles and persevere in the face of adversity.

Born in Tarrytown, New York, Bennett-Smallwood currently resides in Dallas, Texas, with her humble and talented daughter, Jaelyn, and her fur baby, Miracle.

CPSIA information can be obtained
at www.ICGtesting.com
Printed in the USA
BVHW021623141020
591013BV00020B/22

9 781632 964168